HOT WHEELS
BATTLE FORCE 5

Pedigree

Published 2010. Published by Pedigree Books
Limited, Beech Hill House, Walnut Gardens,
Exeter, Devon, EX4 4DH
email: books@pedigreegroup.co.uk
web: www.pedigreebooks.com

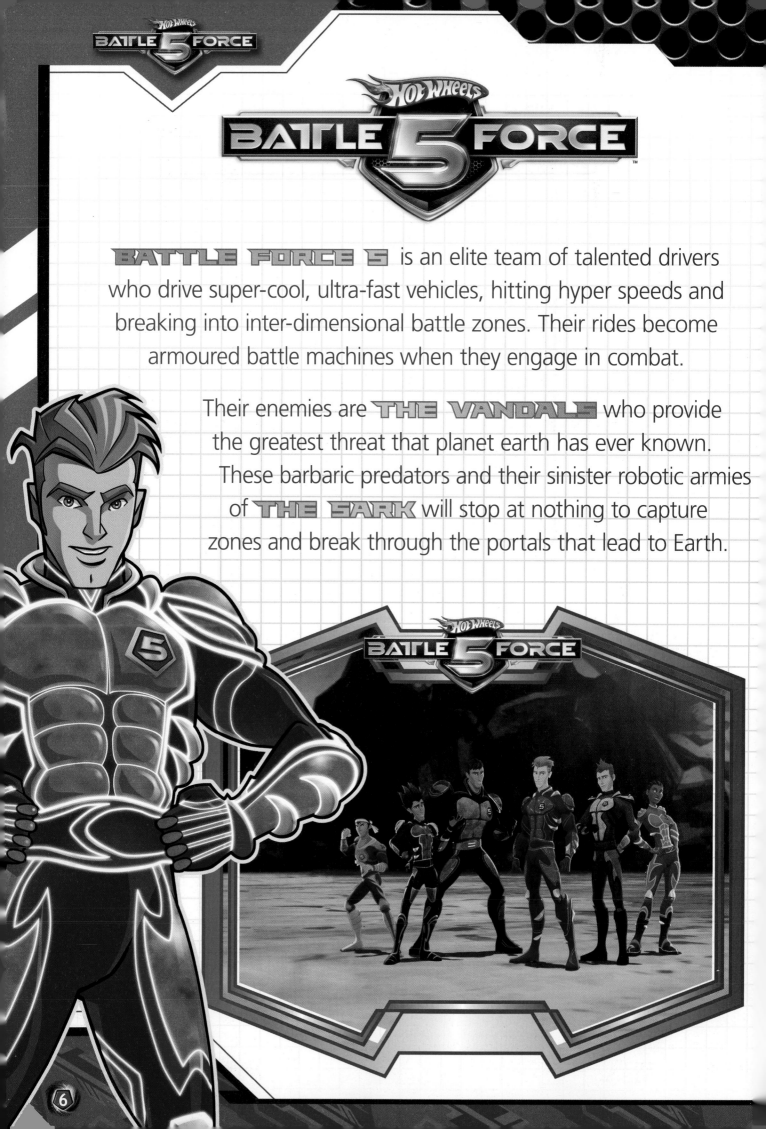

BATTLE FORCE 5 is an elite team of talented drivers who drive super-cool, ultra-fast vehicles, hitting hyper speeds and breaking into inter-dimensional battle zones. Their rides become armoured battle machines when they engage in combat.

Their enemies are **THE VANDALS** who provide the greatest threat that planet earth has ever known. These barbaric predators and their sinister robotic armies of **THE SARK** will stop at nothing to capture zones and break through the portals that lead to Earth.

DRIVER :: STANDFORD ISAAC RHODES IV

A charming, smooth operator who claims to be part of British Royalty. Standford is mad for music, sound and speed. This smooth-talker is an acoustical expert with advanced sensory perception.

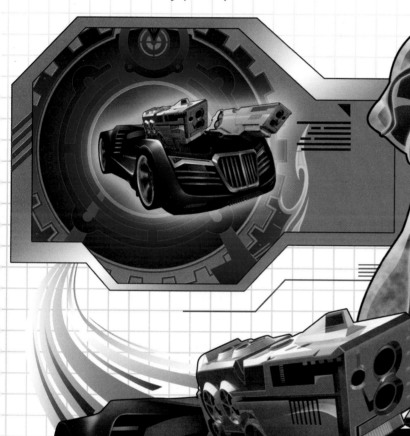

VEHICLE :: REVERB

Outfitted with long-range sonic weapons, Reverb has massive twin guns that blast waves of smashing sound. These deafening blasts can smash its opponents.

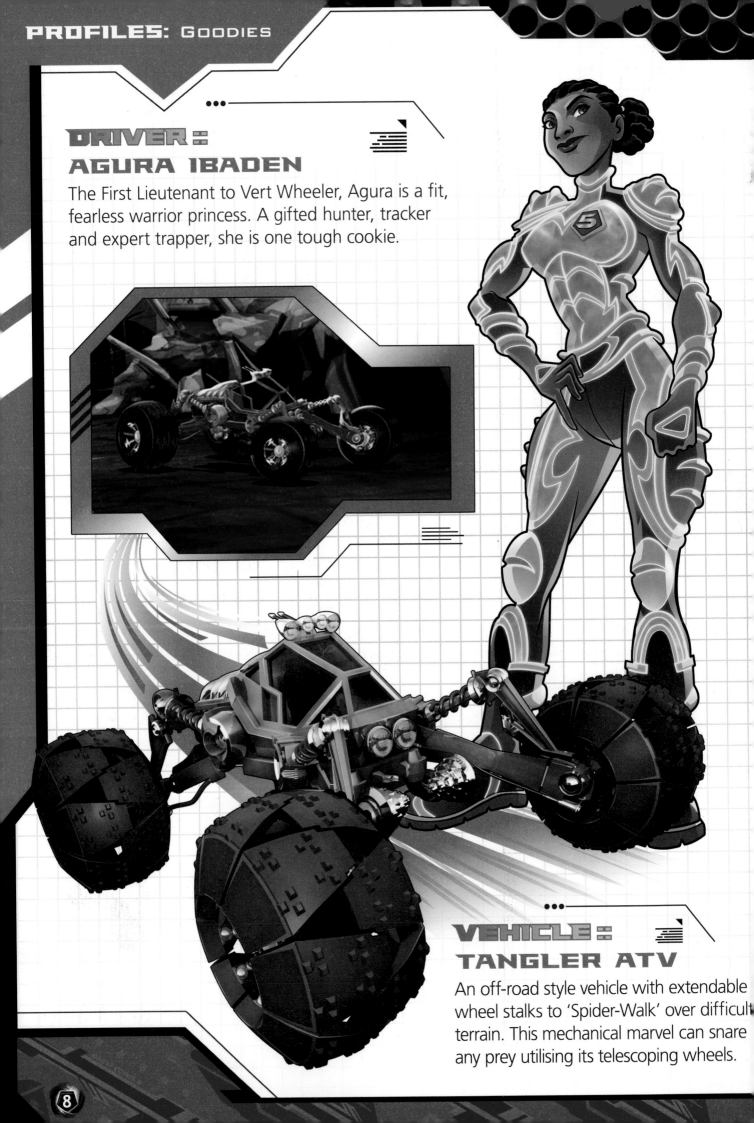

DRIVER ::
AGURA IBADEN

The First Lieutenant to Vert Wheeler, Agura is a fit, fearless warrior princess. A gifted hunter, tracker and expert trapper, she is one tough cookie.

VEHICLE ::
TANGLER ATV

An off-road style vehicle with extendable wheel stalks to 'Spider-Walk' over difficult terrain. This mechanical marvel can snare any prey utilising its telescoping wheels.

DRIVER ::
VERT WHEELER

The leader of Battle Force 5 and the fastest driver on the team, super cool Vert Wheeler is a role model to the rest of the crew, making the tough decisions and offering advice and support along the way.

VEHICLE ::
SABER

An incredibly fast 'first striker' vehicle which is used like a sword. Saber is extremely flexible thanks to a double-sided drive capability and rotating cockpit.

DRIVER ::
ZOOM TAKAZUMI

Zoom is the team's scout and stealth specialist, Zoom a martial arts expert and a thrill seeker. Zoom is also the youngest member of Battle Force 5.

VEHICLE ::
THE CHOPPER

The Chopper is a motorcycle with wheels that can split to turn into propellers for limited flight and can double as blade weapons. It's stealthy and fast and can hover and navigate tight spaces. The wheels also split into blades.

DRIVERS :
SHERMAN AND SPINNER CORTEZ

The two brothers serve as the team's tactical and technical support. Spinner is outgoing, but much smaller and an expert computer hacker. He loves playing practical jokes and is a video game champion. Sherman is strong with more physical presence, but he is also intelligent, a sound mathematician and a mechanical genius.

VEHICLE :
THE BUSTER TANK

The Buster Tank has six wheels and is armed with a turret of spinning chain-maces. Powerful, and loaded with weaponry including circular flails and saw blades, this high-tech tank is not to be messed with.

THE SARK :

Super Robot Species programmed to destroy anything in their way, including the Battle Force 5.

DRIVER = ZEMERIK

Evil leader of The Sark, top ranking super robot entity Zemerik has no feelings, no fears and no inhibitions.

VEHICLE =

ZELIX

A super high-tech machine that is complete with dark matter and energy blades.

DRIVER :
ZURKS

The robotic army of Zemerik that swarms to overtake their prey. Fast and lightweight, the Zurks work as an army to overtake enemies.

VEHICLE :
ZENTNER

Fast and lightweight and made up of dark matter energy spines, the Zentner works as part of an army to swarm and overtake enemies.

DRIVER :
ZUG

Zemerik's heavy-duty henchman and dim-witted enforcer.

VEHICLE :
ZENDRILLS

A rough and tough high-tech vehicle built to bash, batter and brutalise.

THE VANDALS ::

A race of predatory humanoid animals from the distant planet Vandal. They seek to enslave Earth.

CAPTAIN KALUS

The lion-like leader of The Vandals, Captain Kalus rules with fear - using a crossbow mounted on his left arm.

VEHICLE ::

THE FANGORE

A chariot-like, animalistic vehicle armed with a spear launcher on the front and sharp fangs and claws.

DRIVER ::
KROCOMODO

A sneaky crocodile-like creature, Krocomodo plans a conspiracy to become leader of The Vandals.

VEHICLE ::
THE RIPTILE

Armoured buggy with saw blades on the front and spring powered weapons that can either clamp or chomp enemies.

DRIVER :: HATCH

A lobster/insect-like Vandal with menacing stingers and claws.

VEHICLE ::
THE SCARIB

The Scarib, a skeletal looking vehicle armed with a giant stinger tail that can shoot acid into its prey.

DRIVER :: SEVER

Kalus's second in command, this aquatic predator is really mean and out of control.

VEHICLE ::
THE WATER
SLAUGHTER

The Water Slaughter is ultra-fast with has razor-sharp clamping jaw weaponry.

NAME MIX UP

The letters of these ten Battle Force 5 vehicles have been all jumbled up. Their vehicles include those driven by the GOODIES and their enemies the BADDIES. Every single one of them has been called back to the garage and need some serious mechanical work to make them run smoothly. Get your spelling overalls and thinking cap on and try to fix this mess.

1. GERTLAN TAV
☐☐☐☐☐☐☐ ☐☐☐

2. ETH PECHROP
☐☐☐ ☐☐☐☐☐☐☐

3. HET RAWET RASULEGHT
☐☐☐ ☐☐☐☐☐ ☐☐☐☐☐☐☐☐☐

4. NEZRENT
☐☐☐☐☐☐☐

5. TEH GRANFOE
☐☐☐ ☐☐☐☐☐☐☐

6. HET RABSIC
☐☐☐ ☐☐☐☐☐☐

7. BREREV
☐☐☐☐☐☐

8. ETH ITRELIP
☐☐☐ ☐☐☐☐☐☐☐

9. LEXZI
☐☐☐☐☐

10. HET STUBER NAKT
☐☐☐ ☐☐☐☐☐☐ ☐☐☐☐

MATCH THE DRIVERS TO THEIR VEHICLES

Use your knowledge of the battle force GOODIES and their evil enemies the BADDIES to match the right Drivers to their Vehicles. The list of drivers is on the left-hand side with their vehicles on the right.
Draw a line to match them up!

Drivers	Vehicles
SHERMAN CORTEZ	ZENTNER
ZOOM TAKAZUMI	THE RIPTILE
KROCOMODO	THE SCARIB
CAPTAIN KALUS	SABER
AGURA IBADEN	THE BUSTER TANK
VERT WHEELER	THE FANGORE
SEVER	REVERB
HATCH	TANGLER ATV
STANDFORD ISAAC RHODES	THE WATER SLAUGHTER
ZEMERIK	THE CHOPPER

BUMPER
WORDSEARCH

Scan through this grid of letters to find each of the listed BATTLE FORCE 5 related words. The words could be written forwards, backwards, horizontally, vertically and diagonally so keep your eyes peeled to find all 20...

REVERB ☐

ZEMERIK ☐

KALUS ☐

STANDFORD ☐

SABER ☐

TANGLER ATV ☐

SARK ☐

SHERMAN ☐

HATCH ☐

AGURA ☐

ZELIX ☐

ZURKS ☐

SEVER ☐

CHOPPER ☐

VERT ☐

SPINNER ☐

ZENTNER ☐

ZUG ☐

WHEELER ☐

ZOOM ☐

OBSERVATION SPECIAL

1

_ _ _ _ _ _

2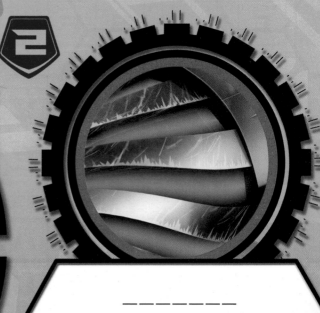

_ _ _ _ _ _ _

4

3

_ _ _ _ _ _ _ _ _ _ _ _ _

_ _ _ _ _ _ _ _ _

The GOODIES and BADDIES have been sending their spies to check out their rivals' vehicles. The spies have taken close up photographs of parts of each vehicle. Scan through the zoomed in pictures of 8 different machines. Can you identify which vehicle is which from these extreme close ups?

A:: REVERB
B:: THE FANGORE
C:: ZENDRIL
D:: SABER
E:: THE CHOPPER
F:: ZENTNER
G:: THE SCARIB
H:: THE BUSTER TANK

___ _____

___ _____

_____

_____

SPOT THE ODD ONE OUT

Scan through these five rows of BATTLE FORCE FIVE characters and vehicles.
One in each row does not match or is slightly different to the others.
Can you spot which one it is?

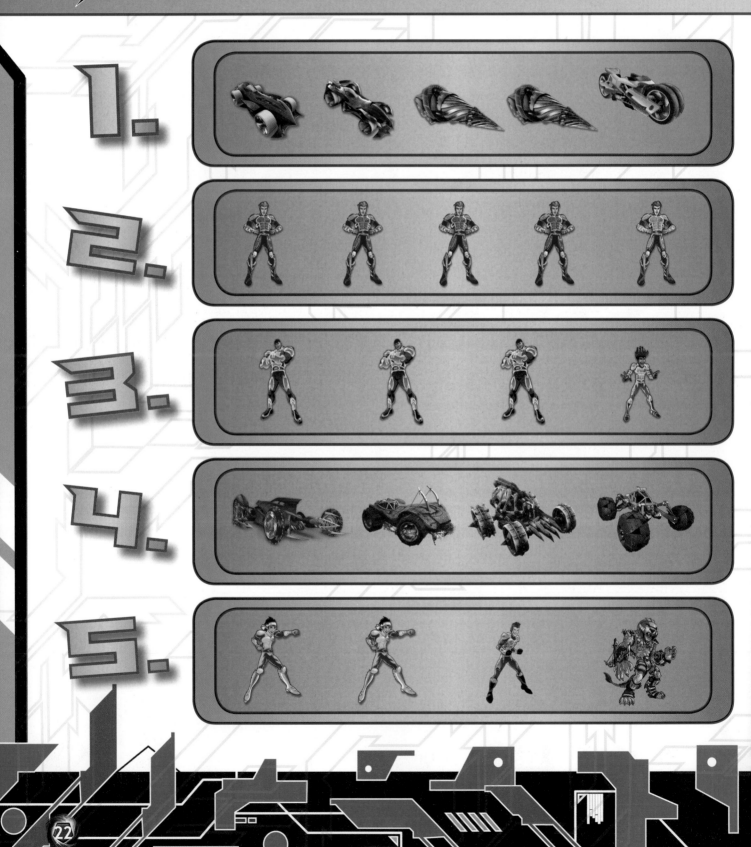

COMPLETE THE DRIVER NAMES

The drivers below are missing most of their letters, fill in the gaps to put all the parts into place to reveal their full name...

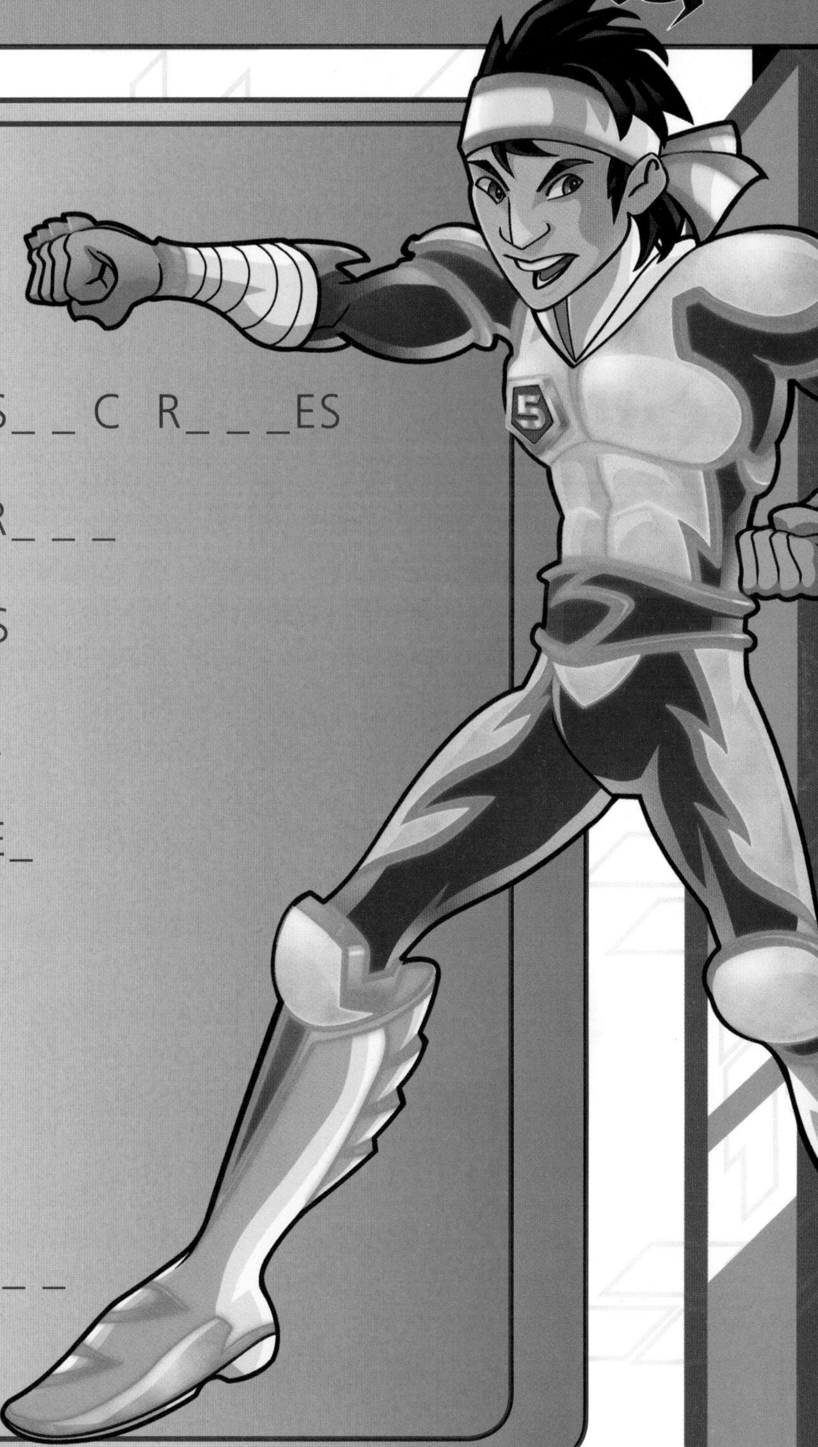

1. _A_C_

2. S_ _N_F_ _D _S_ _ _C R_ _ _ES

3. _ _E_M _N _OR_ _ _

4. C_ _T_I_ _ _L_S

5. _ _UR_ I_ _DE_

6. V_ _ _ _H_ _LE_

7. _E_ _R

8. Z_ _ _R_K

9. _ _ _ _OM_ D_

10. Z_ _ _ T_ _A_U_ _

The Vandals'

Find your way through this maze to escape from the clutches of the BADDIES and prevent falling into the hands of The Vandals.

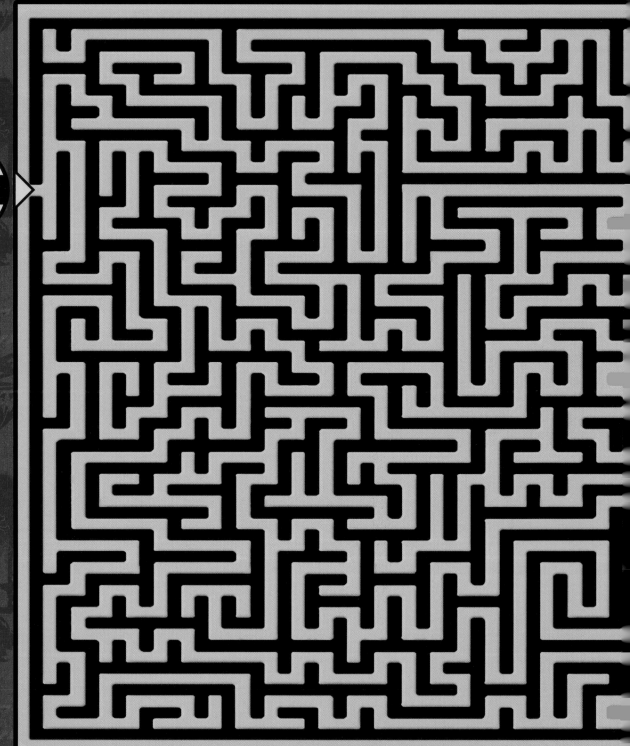

MAZE

FINISH

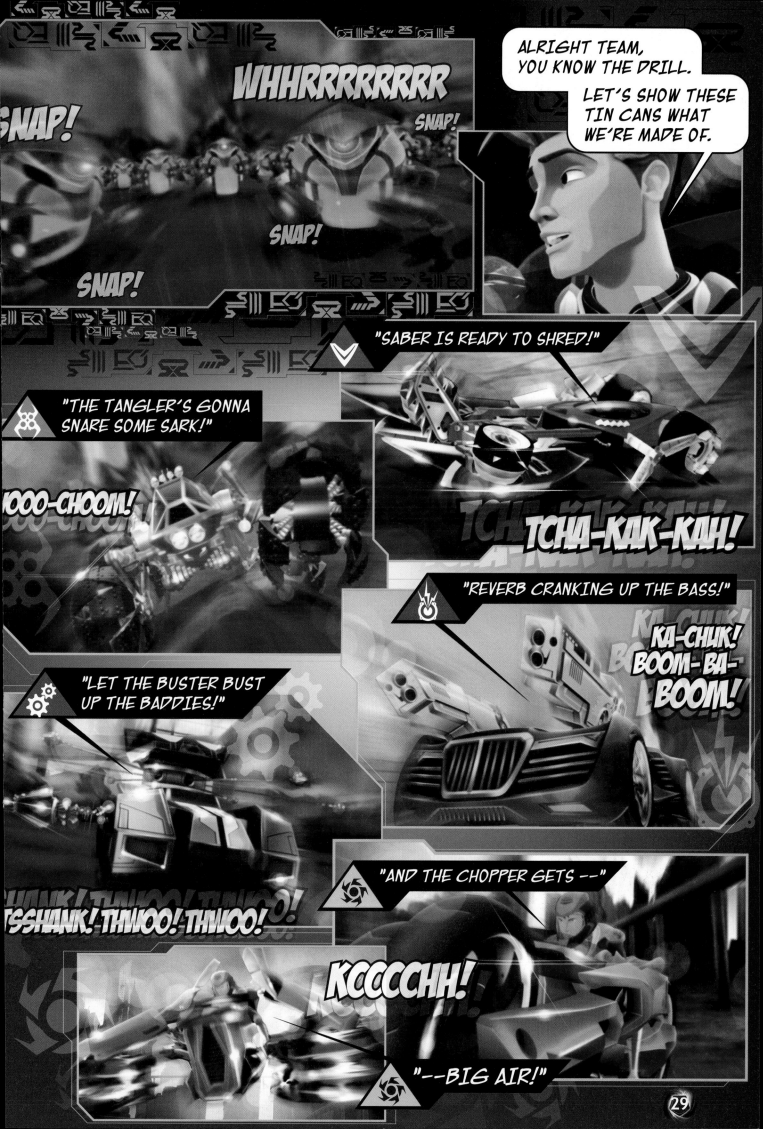

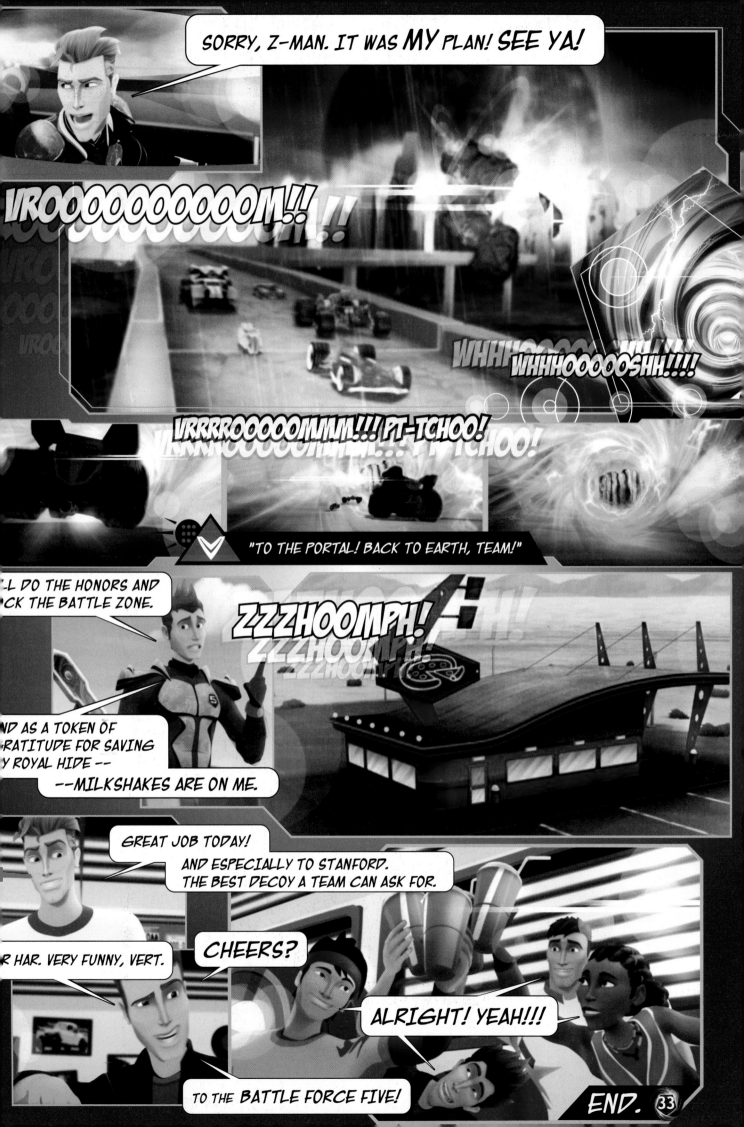

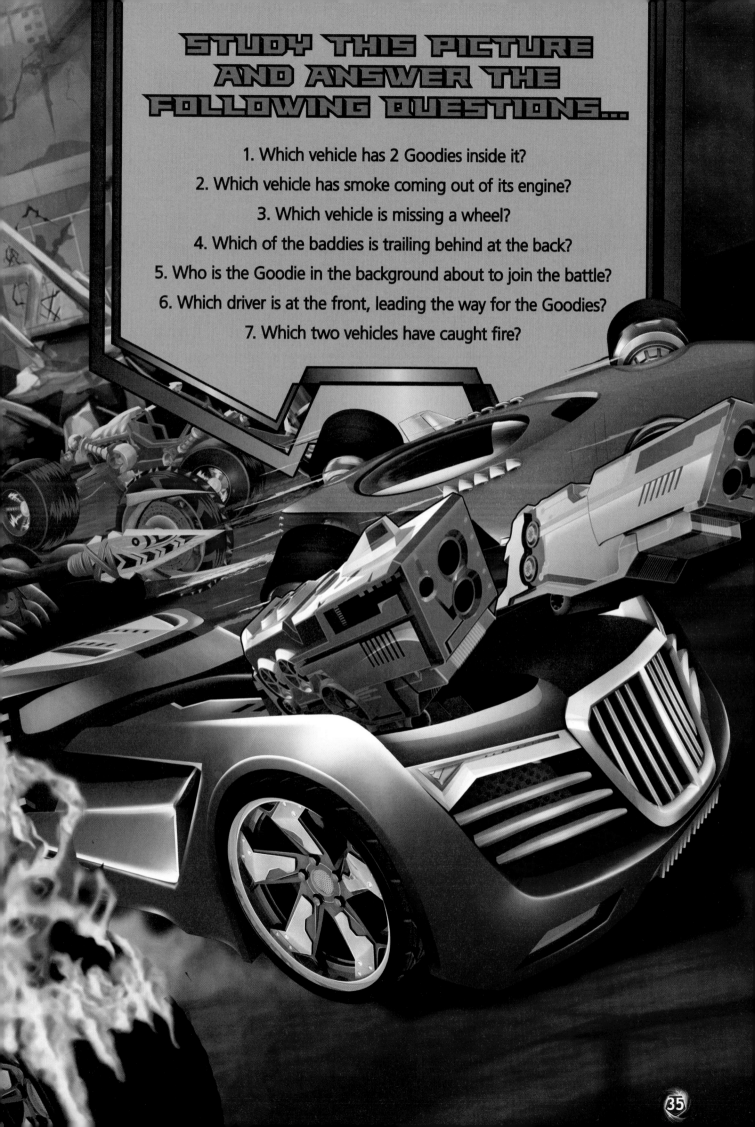

STUDY THIS PICTURE AND ANSWER THE FOLLOWING QUESTIONS...

1. Which vehicle has 2 Goodies inside it?

2. Which vehicle has smoke coming out of its engine?

3. Which vehicle is missing a wheel?

4. Which of the baddies is trailing behind at the back?

5. Who is the Goodie in the background about to join the battle?

6. Which driver is at the front, leading the way for the Goodies?

7. Which two vehicles have caught fire?

WORDSEARCH

Check through this grid of letters to find each of the Battle Force 5 Goodies and Baddies listed below. The names could be written forwards, backwards, horizontally, vertically and diagonally so keep your hands on the wheel and your eyes on the road to find all of them...

STANDFORD ☐

VERT WHEELER ☐

RIPTILE ☐

KROCOMODO ☐

REVERB ☐

SPINNER ☐

ZENTNER ☐

CAPTAIN KALUS ☐

AGURA ☐

SABER ☐

ZEMERIK ☐

FANGORE ☐

ZENDRILLS ☐

SHERMAN ☐

THE SARK ☐

ZOOM ☐

D	E	A	R	U	G	A	K	L	S	O	E	X
D	S	N	X	V	R	I	A	O	P	Z	I	I
P	H	T	N	C	R	K	D	O	I	C	I	X
E	A	C	A	E	J	O	D	E	N	A	T	B
T	T	T	B	N	M	M	R	P	N	P	P	R
Q	I	A	T	O	F	E	B	V	E	T	E	E
C	S	W	C	R	N	O	H	U	R	A	R	V
D	F	O	U	T	F	F	R	D	E	I	X	E
I	R	N	N	T	R	E	W	D	C	N	V	R
K	I	E	M	K	O	L	R	F	S	K	L	S
A	Z	H	N	J	K	I	L	P	S	A	A	T
Y	N	H	J	M	D	G	H	Y	U	L	L	S
Z	E	N	D	R	I	L	L	S	T	U	N	V
A	O	Y	H	B	V	G	F	H	C	S	R	F
K	I	R	E	M	E	Z	E	D	F	W	L	O
X	C	K	M	H	T	S	F	V	B	N	R	E
P	I	O	C	D	A	M	B	H	J	K	O	P
E	O	D	G	R	J	U	V	N	M	K	L	O
Z	I	L	K	H	A	N	A	M	R	E	H	S
B	L	L	K	C	A	E	R	O	G	N	A	F
R	E	L	E	E	H	W	T	R	E	V	O	P

SPOT THE DIFFERENCE

Scan through these two pictures of the Vandals in hot pursuit of Battle Force 5 heroes. Try to spot the five differences...

MATCH THE CAR TO THE CORRECT NAME

- REVERB
- TANGLER ATV
- SABER
- THE BUSTER TANK
- THE CHOPPER
- THE RIPTILE
- ZELIX
- THE FANGORE
- THE SCARIB
- THE WATER SLAUGHTER

BATTLE FORCE 5

BATTLE FORCE 5

BATTLE FORCE 5

BATTLE FORCE 5

BATTLE FORCE 5

LOOK THROUGH THE COOL PICTURES OF THESE 10 BATTLE FORCE 5 VEHICLES. SOME OF THEM ARE THE GOODIES' CARS AND SOME ARE DRIVEN BY THE BADDIES. CHECK THE LIST OF NAMES AND MATCH THEM TO THE CORRECT CAR.

BATTLE FORCE 5

BATTLE FORCE 5

BATTLE FORCE 5

BATTLE FORCE 5

RED LIGHT GREEN LIGHT

1. **REVERB** has massive twin guns which blast deafening waves of smashing sound.

2. **AGURA** is one of the Baddies.

3. **VERT WHEELER** drives the **SABER.**

4. **ZOOM TAKAZUMI** drives the **MONSTER MOPED** ⊗☐ ⊗☐

5. **SHERMAN'S** brother is called **PINNER.** ⊗☐ ⊗☐

6. The **VANDALS** hail from the planet **VANDAL.**

Read through these statements about the **BATTLE FORCE 5** heroes and the baddies from **THE SARK** and **THE VANDALS** and work out which ones are true **[GREEN LIGHTS]** or false **[RED LIGHTS]** and tick the right coloured box...

7. **ZEMERIC'S** robotic army is called the **BURKS**.

8. **KROCOMODO** drives **THE REPTILE**.

9. **HATCH** can be best described as an insect-like Vandal with menacing stingers and claws.

10. **SHERMAN** and **SPINNER'S** last name is **GARCIA**.

11. **CAPTAIN KALUS** is the leader of **THE VANDALS**.

12. **SEVER** usually drives **THE WATER SLAUGHTER**.

13. **CAPTAIN KALUS** is best friends with **VERT WHEELER**

14. **SPINNER AND SHERMAN** can usually be found behind the wheel of **THE BUSTER TANK**.

15. **STANDFORD ISAAC RHODES IV** is an acoustical expert.

HOT WHEELS BATTLE 5 FORCE

JANUARY

M	T	W	T	F	S	S
					1	2
3	4	5	6	7	8	9
10	11	12	13	14	15	16
17	18	19	20	21	22	23
24	25	26	27	28	29	30
31						

FEBRUARY

M	T	W	T	F	S	S
1	2	3	4	5	6	
7	8	9	10	11	12	13
14	15	16	17	18	19	20
21	22	23	24	25	26	27
28						

MARCH

M	T	W	T	F	S	S
	1	2	3	4	5	6
7	8	9	10	11	12	13
14	15	16	17	18	19	20
21	22	23	24	25	26	27
28	29	30	31			

APRIL

M	T	W	T	F	S	S
				1	2	3
4	5	6	7	8	9	10
11	12	13	14	15	16	17
18	19	20	21	22	23	24
25	26	27	28	29	30	

MAY

M	T	W	T	F	S	S
						1
2	3	4	5	6	7	8
9	10	11	12	13	14	15
16	17	18	19	20	21	22
23	24	25	26	27	28	29
30	31					

JUNE

M	T	W	T	F	S	S
		1	2	3	4	5
6	7	8	9	10	11	12
13	14	15	16	17	18	19
20	21	22	23	24	25	26
27	28	29	30			

CALENDAR 2011

JULY

M	T	W	T	F	S	S
				1	2	3
4	5	6	7	8	9	10
11	12	13	14	15	16	17
18	19	20	21	22	23	24
25	26	27	28	29	30	31

AUGUST

M	T	W	T	F	S	S
1	2	3	4	5	6	7
8	9	10	11	12	13	14
15	16	17	18	19	20	21
22	23	24	25	26	27	28
29	30	31				

SEPTEMBER

M	T	W	T	F	S	S
			1	2	3	4
5	6	7	8	9	10	11
12	13	14	15	16	17	18
19	20	21	22	23	24	25
26	27	28	29	30		

OCTOBER

M	T	W	T	F	S	S
					1	2
3	4	5	6	7	8	9
10	11	12	13	14	15	16
17	18	19	20	21	22	23
24	25	26	27	28	29	30
31						

NOVEMBER

M	T	W	T	F	S	S
	1	2	3	4	5	6
7	8	9	10	11	12	13
14	15	16	17	18	19	20
21	22	23	24	25	26	27
28	29	30				

DECEMBER

M	T	W	T	F	S	S
			1	2	3	4
5	6	7	8	9	10	11
12	13	14	15	16	17	18
19	20	21	22	23	24	25
26	27	28	29	30	31	

ANSWERS

P16 – NAME MIX UP

1–TANGLER ATV, 2–THE CHOPPER,
3–THE WATER SLAUGHTER, 4–ZENTNER, 5–THE FANGORE,
6–THE SCARIB, 7–REVERB,   8–THE RIPTILE, 9–ZELIX
10–THE BUSTER TANK.

P17 – MATCH THE DRIVER TO THEIR VEHICLE

SHERMAN CORTEZ	– THE BUSTER TANK
ZOOM TAKAZUMI	– THE CHOPPER
KROCOMODO	– THE REPTILE
CAPTAIN KALUS	– THE FANGORE
AGURA IBADEN	– TANGLER ATV
VERT WHEELER	– SABER
SEVER	– THE WATER SLAUGHTER
HATCH	– THE SCARIB
STANDFORD ISAAC RHODES	– REVERB
ZEMERIK	– ZENTNER.

P18 – BUMPER WORDSEARCH

P20 – BATTLE FORCE 5 OBSERVATION SPECIAL

The 8 Vehicles... REVERB, THE FANGORE, THE RIPTILE,
SABER, THE CHOPPER, ZENTNER, THE SCARIB,
THE BUSTER TANK.

P22 – SPOT THE ODD ONE OUT

First Row...	THE CHOPPER
Second Row...	5 VERT WHEELERS, but one with different coloured clothing
Third Row...	1 SPINNER CORTEZ
Fourth Row...	TANGLER ATV
Fifth Row...	1 CAPTAIN KALUS.

P23 – COMPLETE THE DRIVER NAMES

1–HATCH, 2–STANDFORD ISAAC RHODES, 3–SHERMAN CORTEZ,
4–CAPTAIN KALUS, 5–AGURA IBADEN, 6–VERT WHEELER,
7–SEVER, 8–ZEMERIK, 9–KROCOMODO, 10–ZOOM TAKAZUMI.

P24 – THE VANDALS' MAZE

P34 – OBSERVATION QUIZ

1–4 from REVERB, SABER, THE BUSTER TANK, TANGLER ATV, THE
FANGORE, THE RIPTILE, THE WATER SLAUGHTER and THE SCARIB,
2–THE BUSTER TANK, 3–THE SCARIB, 4–THE BUSTER TANK and
THE FANORE, 5–8, 6–THE WATER SLAUGHTER, 7–THE SCARIB,
8–ZOOM TAKAZUMI,9–STANFORD RHODES, 10–THE RIPTILE
and THE SCARIB.

P36 – BUMPER BATTLE FORCE 5 WORDSEARCH

Page 37 – SPOT THE DIFFERENCE

P38 – MATCH THE CAR TO THE CORRECT NAME

Look through the cool pictures of these 10 Battle Force 5
vehicles. Some of them are the goodies cars and some are
driven by the baddies. Check the list of names and match
them to the correct car.

△ REVERB - RED TRIANGLE
△ TANGLER ATV - GREEN TRIANGLE
△ SABER - ORANGE TRIANGLE
△ THE BUSTER TANK - PURPLE TRIANGLE
△ THE CHOPPER - DARK BLUE TRIANGLE
△ THE RIPTILE - GREY TRIANGLE
△ ZELIX - LIGHT YELLOW TRIANGLE
△ THE FANGORE - LIGHT BLUE TRIANGLE
△ THE SCARIB - DARK YELLOW TRIANGLE
△ THE WATER SLAUGHTER - BLACK TRIANGLE.

P40 – BATTLE FORCE FIVE GREEN LIGHT RED LIGHT

1–Green Light, 2–Red Light, 3–Green Light, 4–Red Light,
5–Red Light, 6–Green Light, 7–Red Light, 8–Green Light,
9–Green Light, 10–Red Light, 11–Green Light, 12–Green Light,
13–Red Light, 14–Green Light, 15–Green Light.

CONTENTS

Pedigree

Published 2010. Published by Pedigree Books
Limited, Beech Hill House, Walnut Gardens,
Exeter, Devon, EX4 4DH
email: books@pedigreegroup.co.uk
web: www.pedigreebooks.com

£7.99

CAR PROFILES

HOT WHEELS ARE WITHOUT QUESTION THE COOLEST METAL CARS IN THE WORLD. HOW MANY HAVE YOU COLLECTED SO FAR? MAYBE YOU'VE GOT A FEW, MAYBE A FEW HUNDRED OR MAYBE YOU'RE JUST ABOUT TO START YOUR COLLECTION. EITHER WAY THESE PROFILES WILL GIVE YOU LOADS OF INFO ABOUT SOME OF MOST POPULAR MACHINES...

MOTORSPORTS CARS

TOP SPEED:
185MPH
0 - 60MPH:
3.9 SECS
ENGINE: V10
POWER:
623 BHP

24 SEVEN

SUZUKA

TOP SPEED:
199MPH
0 - 60MPH:
3.8 SECS
ENGINE: V12
POWER:
505 BHP

TOP SPEED:
180 MPH
0 - 60MPH:
4.5 SECS
ENGINE: V8
POWER:
360 BHP

FAST FISH

HARD DRIVE

TOP SPEED:
211MPH
0 - 60MPH:
4.4 SECS
ENGINE: V6
POWER:
540 BHP

CAR PROFILES

TWIN MILL

TOP SPEED:
195MPH
0 - 60MPH:
3.2 SECS
ENGINE: V10
POWER:
627 BHP

URBAN AGENT

TOP SPEED:
203MPH
0 - 60MPH:
3.8 SECS
ENGINE: V8
POWER:
346 BHP

ZOTIC

TOP SPEED:
209MPH
0 - 60MPH:
3.5 SECS
ENGINE: V10
POWER:
356 BHP

ULTRA RAGE

TOP SPEED:
218 MPH
0 - 60MPH:
4.8 SECS
ENGINE: V10
POWER:
310 BHP

JACK HAMMER

TOP SPEED:
198MPH
0 - 60MPH:
3.9 SECS
ENGINE: V8
POWER:
523 BHP

CAR PROFILES

TOP SPEED:
175MPH
0 - 60MPH:
4.6 SECS
ENGINE: V6
POWER:
356 BHP

CIRCLE TRACKER

OVERBOARD 454

TOP SPEED:
198 MPH
0 - 60MPH:
4.6 SECS
ENGINE: V12
POWER:
550 BHP

TOP SPEED:
210MPH
0 - 60MPH:
3.2 SECS
ENGINE: V12
POWER:
440 BHP

PARADOX

TOP SPEED:
178MPH
0 - 60MPH:
4.1 SECS
ENGINE: V6
POWER:
511 BHP

JET THREAT

TOP SPEED:
204 MPH
0 - 60MPH:
3.7 SECS
ENGINE: V8
POWER:
411 BHP

ROCKET FIRE

CAR PROFILES

COOL ONE

TOP SPEED:
206MPH
0 - 60MPH:
4.3 SECS
ENGINE: V12
POWER:
445 BHP

DRAGSTER

TOP SPEED:
198MPH
0 - 60MPH:
4.2 SECS
ENGINE: V8
POWER:
438 BHP

SPINE BUSTER

TOP SPEED:
204MPH
0 - 60MPH:
3.5 SECS
ENGINE: V10
POWER:
450 BHP

BULLY GOAT

TOP SPEED:
203MPH
0 - 60MPH:
4.5 SECS
ENGINE: V6
POWER:
510 BHP

CAR PROFILES

NITRO DOORSLAMMER

TOP SPEED:
190 MPH
0 – 60MPH:
5.8 SECS
ENGINE: V8
POWER:
375 BHP

PROTOTYPE H-24

TOP SPEED:
210MPH
0 – 60MPH:
3.9 SECS
ENGINE: V12
POWER:
615 BHP

MED EVIL

TOP SPEED:
216 MPH
0 – 60MPH:
3.4 SECS
ENGINE: V8
POWER:
415 BHP

CALIFORNIA CUSTOM CARS

BONE SHAKER

TOP SPEED:
197MPH
0 – 60MPH:
3.2 SECS
ENGINE: V10
POWER:
627 BHP

CAR PROFILES

BASSLINE

TOP SPEED:
217MPH
0 - 60MPH:
3.6 SECS
ENGINE: V10
POWER:
500 BHP

ROCKET BOX

TOP SPEED:
160MPH
0 - 60MPH:
3.4 SECS
ENGINE: V6
POWER:
650 BHP

RIVITED

TOP SPEED:
200 MPH
0 - 60MPH:
4.3 SECS
ENGINE: V6
POWER:
444 BHP

RODGER DODGER

TOP SPEED:
207MPH
0 - 60MPH:
3.1 SECS
ENGINE: V12
POWER:
665 BHP

SOOO FAST

TOP SPEED:
186 MPH
0 - 60MPH:
4.2 SECS
ENGINE: V8
POWER:
370 BHP

CAR PROFILES

TOP SPEED:
217 MPH
0 - 60MPH:
3.7 SECS
ENGINE: V10
POWER:
570 BHP

SURF CRATE

TOP SPEED:
210 MPH
0 - 60MPH:
3.2 SECS
ENGINE: V8
POWER:
359 BHP

RATBOMB

TOP SPEED:
195MPH
0 - 60MPH:
3.4 SECS
ENGINE: V12
POWER:
645 BHP

PURPLE PASSION

TOP SPEED:
203MPH
0 - 60MPH:
4.4 SECS
ENGINE: V12
POWER:
505 BHP

HOLLOWBACK

TOP SPEED:
222 MPH
0 - 60MPH:
3.2 SECS
ENGINE: V6
POWER:
479 BHP

DEORA

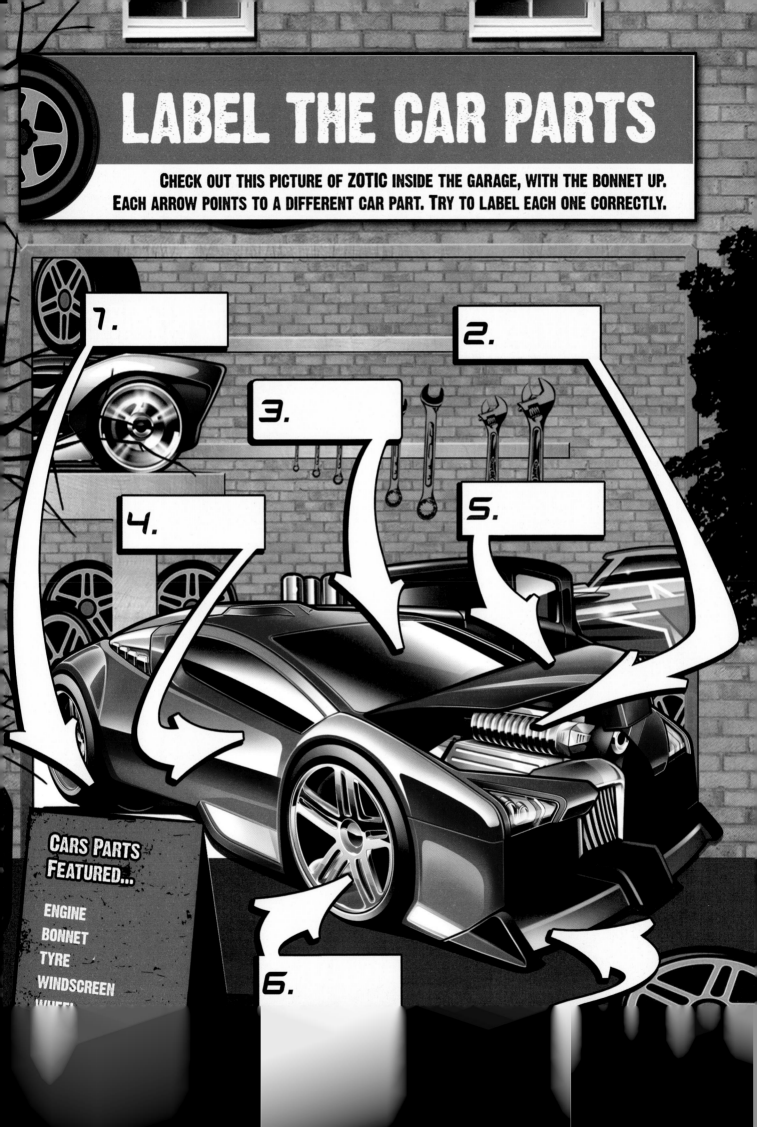

LABEL THE CAR PARTS

CHECK OUT THIS PICTURE OF ZOTIC INSIDE THE GARAGE, WITH THE BONNET UP.
EACH ARROW POINTS TO A DIFFERENT CAR PART. TRY TO LABEL EACH ONE CORRECTLY.

7.

2.

3.

4.

5.

CARS PARTS
FEATURED...

ENGINE
BONNET
TYRE
WINDSCREEN
WHEEL

6.

PIT STOP

DESIGN YOUR OWN HOTWHEELS CAR

NOW IT'S TIME TO TURN OFF THE IGNITION, CHANGE INTO NEUTRAL AND USE THIS PAGE TO DESIGN YOUR VERY OWN HOT WHEELS VEHICLE. USING SOME OF THE EXISTING CARS FOR INSPIRATION, SKETCH OUT YOUR DREAM MACHINE OR LET YOUR IMAGINATION REV THROUGH THE GEARS TO DRAW THE PLANS OF A VEHICLE THAT CAN COMPETE WITH THE FASTEST AND MOST POWERFUL HOT WHEELS.

HOT WHEELS NAME MIX UP

The letters of these ten Hot Wheels cars have been all jumbled up. They've been called back to the garage and need some serious mechanical work to make them run smoothly. Get your spelling overalls and thinking cap on and try to fix this mess.

1. RUFS EATCR
_ _ _ _   _ _ _ _ _

2. ARTUL GARE
_ _ _ _ _   _ _ _ _

3. TAR MOBB
_ _ _   _ _ _ _

4. COTIZ
_ _ _ _ _

5. OLOC NOE
_ _ _ _   _ _ _

6. KAZUSU
_ _ _ _ _ _

7. BRANU NETAG
_ _ _ _ _   _ _ _ _ _

8. NESPI STUBER
_ _ _ _ _   _ _ _ _ _ _

9. NITW LIML
_ _ _ _   _ _ _ _

10. 42 NESEV
_ _   _ _ _ _ _

CLUES:
URBAN AGENT
SURF CRATE
ULTRA RAGE
24 SEVEN
TWIN MILL
RAT BOMB
ZOTIC
COOL ONE
SUZUKA
SPINE BUSTER

SPOT THE DIFFERENCE

Check out these two pictures of RODGER DODGER and COOL ONE racing around the track. There are seven differences between picture 1 and picture 2. Can you spot them all?

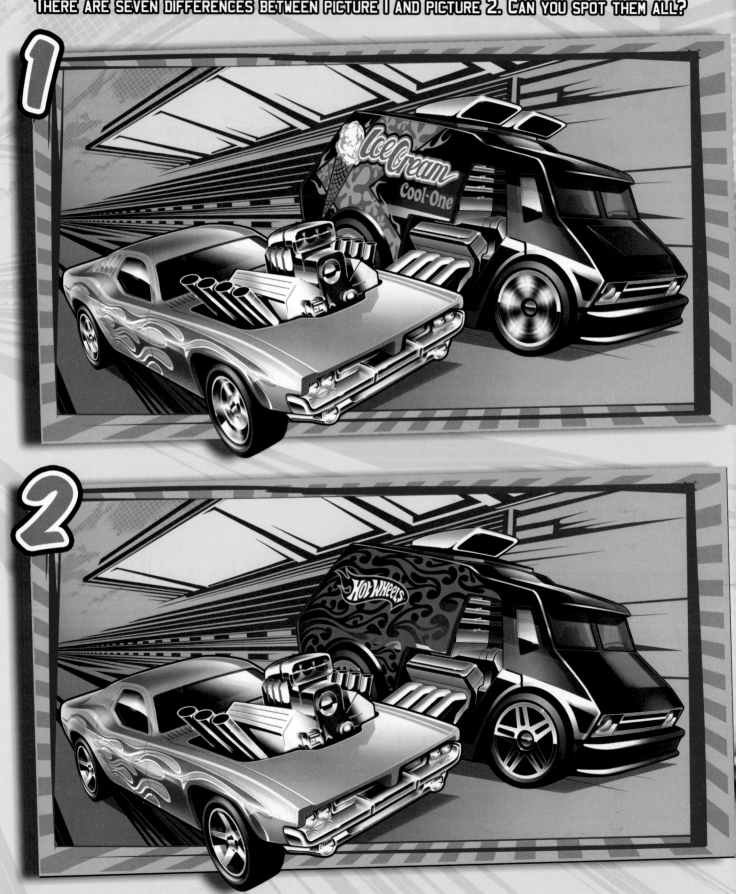

BUMPER WORDSEARCH

Scan through this grid of letters to find each of the listed car-related words. The words could be written forwards, backwards, horizontally, vertically and diagonally so keep your eyes peeled to find all 20...

Word list:
- WHEELS
- EXHAUST
- FUEL
- WIPERS
- ENGINE
- WINDSCREEN
- SKID
- RADIATOR
- TYRE
- MIRROR
- SPIN
- JETS
- GEARS
- PETROL
- REV
- STEERING WHEEL
- BREAKS
- OIL
- PITS
- LIGHTS

S	F	H	V	N	E	N	I	G	N	E	P	I
C	L	J	S	F	D	L	T	X	S	T	E	L
B	L	E	D	W	O	Z	A	E	S	T	E	B
I	I	B	E	R	L	B	S	R	W	U	Q	A
C	O	P	T	H	E	L	E	Y	F	D	S	X
Q	Y	E	O	V	W	P	W	U	S	T	S	W
C	P	K	L	P	I	Y	T	T	E	D	S	T
H	Y	M	D	W	U	J	E	P	T	Z	Y	E
U	O	V	B	N	M	J	D	T	S	R	N	L
Y	R	C	V	I	S	D	F	G	E	J	K	S
P	T	E	N	P	I	Y	T	R	F	V	M	T
E	P	B	V	S	D	L	L	E	M	O	I	H
X	R	A	D	I	A	T	O	R	C	J	R	G
H	B	N	M	H	G	V	F	T	Y	U	R	I
A	D	L	C	S	K	A	E	R	B	D	O	L
U	T	I	N	K	L	P	O	P	S	X	R	F
S	G	N	K	K	L	O	D	W	U	E	F	X
T	G	H	J	S	Y	V	B	N	S	T	I	P
L	E	E	H	W	G	N	I	R	E	E	T	S
S	J	F	N	E	E	R	C	S	D	N	I	W
S	P	G	E	A	R	S	V	B	N	K	L	L

HOT WHEELS GRAND PRIX

On a beautiful sunny day in Melbourne, Australia, the drivers and mechanics were ready for the first-ever Hot Wheels Grand Prix. Before the race could start each car had to complete qualifying laps for places on the grid. The fastest car would start in POLE POSITION.

CAR PROFILES

THE FIVE CARS TAKING PART IN THE INAUGURAL HOT WHEELS GRAND PRIX ARE PERFECTLY SUITED TO THE CHALLENGES OF THE TRACK. WITH BREAK-NECK TOP SPEEDS AND PLENTY OF HORSE POWER, THESE PETROL-GUZZLERS SHOULD EASILY EAT UP THE TWISTS AND TURNS OF THE CIRCUIT.

PROTOTYPE H24

TOP SPEED: 210MPH
0-60MPH: 3.9 SECS
ENGINE: V12
POWER: 615 BHP

NUMBERS GUIDE

A QUICK AND SIMPLE GUIDE TO WHAT THE PERFORMANCE FIGURES AND LETTERS MEAN.

MPH – MILES PER HOUR
SECS – SECONDS
BHP – BRAKE HORSE POWER

MERCY BREAKER

TOP SPEED: 212MPH
0-60MPH: 4.1 SECS
ENGINE: V10
POWER: 626 BHP

HARD DRIVE

TOP SPEED: 211MPH
0-60MPH: 4.4 SECS
ENGINE: V6
POWER: 540 BHP

ULTRA RAGE

TOP SPEED: 218 MPH
0-60MPH: 4.8 SECS
ENGINE: V10
POWER: 310 BHP

MED EVIL

TOP SPEED: 216 MPH
0-60MPH: 3.4 SECS
ENGINE: V8
POWER: 415 BHP

EACH CAR WAS ALLOWED THREE LAPS. HALFWAY THROUGH QUALIFICATION THERE WAS ONLY A FRACTION OF A SECOND BETWEEN MED EVIL, HARD DRIVE, AND ULTRA RAGE. ULTRA RAGE HELD THE ADVANTAGE THANKS TO FASTER ACCELERATION. PROTOTYPE H24 AND MERCY BREAKER WERE STRUGGLING TO KEEP PACE.

AFTER THE FINAL QUALIFYING LAP, HARD DRIVE PIPPED ULTRA RAGE BY JUST ONE HUNDREDTH OF A SECOND. HARD DRIVE WOULD BE ON POLE, ULTRA RAGE SECOND ON THE GRID, FOLLOWED BY MED EVIL, PROTOTYPE H24 AND MERCY BREAKER.

AND WAITED FOR THE RED LIGHTS TO
TURN GREEN, THE CROWD CHEERED AND
SCREAMED. THE GREEN LIGHT BULBS
FLASHED, THE TYRES SCREECHED
AND **ULTRA RAGE** SPED AHEAD
OF **HARD DRIVE** TURNING INTO
THE FIRST BEND IN THE LEAD.

THE DRIVER OF MERCY BREAKER STRUGGLED WITH
THE TRACK AFTER SELECTING THE WRONG SET OF
TYRES AND QUICKLY HAD TO CRUISE INTO THE PIT
LANE. IT WAS A COSTLY MISTAKE AS THE OTHER
CARS SOON BUILT A GOOD LEAD.

WITH FRESHLY FITTED TYRES, MERCY BREAKER'S
DRIVER SPED BACK ONTO THE TRACK AND BEGAN
TAKING THE CORNERS AT HUGE SPEEDS. HE SOON
CLOSED IN ON PROTOTYPE H24.

PROTOTYPE WAS STUCK BEHIND MED EVIL, WHOSE DRIVER SEEMED TO BE HAVING A FEW MECHANICAL PROBLEMS. MERCY BREAKER APPROACHED THEM BOTH AT GREAT SPEED!

Soon all three cars were within touching distance and battling for third. With ten laps gone it was clear that two separate races were going on... one for first, between ULTRA RAGE and HARD DRIVE and one for third between the other cars.

ULTRA RAGE and HARD DRIVE weaved in and out of the tight bends, regularly exchanging the lead. The race for third was even more exciting as the drivers took bigger risks.

As they approached a tight chicane the drivers of
MERCY BREAKER and **PROTOTYPE H24** were so close
that they clipped wheels! Both cars spun off the track.
Neither driver was hurt but the cars were out of the race.
MED EVIL's driver knew that third place was secured.

WITH TWO LAPS REMAINING AND MERCY BREAKER GETTING CLOSER, ULTRA RAGE'S DRIVER DECIDED TO PUT THE PEDDLE TO THE METAL TO SPEED AHEAD OF HARD DRIVE ON THE STRAIGHT. THE FANS WHOOPED AND CHEERED IN APPRECIATION AS THE SMOKE FROM THE WHEEL SPINS DRIFTED UP FROM THE TRACK AMIDST THE DEAFENING WHIR OF THE POWERFUL ENGINES.

ULTRA RAGE LEFT THE OTHER TWO VEHICLES TRAILING AS HE CONTINUED TO SET RECORD LAPS. MERCY BREAKER WAS GAINING ON HARD DRIVE AND THE TWO WERE ALMOST LEVEL AS THEY WENT INTO THE CORNERS. MERCY BREAKER'S DRIVER ALMOST LOST CONTROL AS HIS BACK TYRES BEGAN TO SKID.

BOTH DRIVERS WERE SO FOCUSED THEY HADN'T NOTICED THE THICK GREY SMOKE COMING FROM THE EXHAUST OF ULTRA RAGE. IT WAS THE FINAL STRAIGHT AND JUST A FEW SECONDS FROM THE CHEQUERED FLAG. ULTRA RACE HAD GAINED A MASSIVE LEAD BUT THE OTHER TWO CARS WERE QUICKLY CLOSING.

As all three cars approached the finishing line the spectators strained to see who had won. All three vehicles were very close together and the smoke and blur of the high speeds made it almost impossible to tell who had won. The driver had radioed into the team garage with an engine problem. They told him to try and get across the line. But the car was losing speed by the

WHAT A START, WHAT A FINISH, WHAT A RACE!

SECOND WITH **MERCY BREAKER** AND **HARD DRIVE** CLOSING. THEY DIDN'T HAVE TO WAIT TOO LONG, AS THE RACE ANNOUNCER PROVIDED THE RESULTS... **ULTRA RAGE** HAD HELD ON DESPITE HIS ENGINE PROBLEMS.

THE DRIVER PUMPED HIS FIST IN RELIEF AND DELIGHT. SECOND WENT TO **MERCY BREAKER** WHO HAD GOT AHEAD OF **HARD DRIVE** WHO FINISHED THIRD.

RACETRACK DOT TO DOT

JOIN UP THE DOTS TO REVEAL THIS TRICKY, TWISTING RACETRACK. DRAW THE LINES AS NEATLY AS YOU CAN TO MAKE IT AS EASY AS POSSIBLE. WE'VE MADE A START IN THE BOTTOM RIGHT CORNER...

40 41
39 42
16
17
38 15 43
18 14 44
37 13 45
36 19 12 46
35 11
10 20 47
34 48 22
49 21 23
33 32 30 31 29 24
28
27 25
26

9
8
7
6
50
5 51
52
53
4 54
3 55
2 56
1

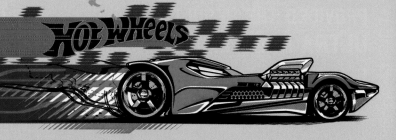

PIT STOP

COLOUR-BY-NUMBERS POSTER

GIVE YOUR ENGINE CHANCE TO COOL DOWN BY TAKING TIME OUT TO COLOUR IN THIS PICTURE OF PROTOTYPE H24. CHECK OUT THE COLOUR AND NUMBERS KEY TO MAKE SURE YOU GET THE PAINT JOB JUST RIGHT TO LET THIS SMOOTH RIDE COME ALIVE ON THE PAGE.

CAR QUIZ

TIME TO CHECK OUT YOUR HOT WHEELS AND GENERAL CAR KNOWLEDGE NOW WITH A BUMPER QUIZ. THERE ARE 20 CHALLENGING TEASERS, SO TRY TO KEEP ON TRACK.

REMEMBER SOME OF THE INFORMATION YOU'VE ALREADY READ AND ANSWER AS MANY AS YOU CAN CORRECTLY...

PLEASE DRIVE CAREFULLY

NO WAY!

1. Which of these three Hot Wheels is spelt incorrectly: SPINE BUSTER ☐ ZODIC ☐ and ☐ 24 SEVEN?

2. What size Engine does PARADOX have, V12 ☐ or V10 ☐?

3. Which Hot Wheel has a similar shape to a van, ROCKET FIRE ☐ RAT BOMB ☐ or COOL ONE ☐?

4. Which vehicle is more powerful PURPLE PASSION ☐ or RIVITED ☐?

5. JET THREAT has an impressive BHP of 511, but what does BHP stand for?

6. BASSLINE has a banging top speed of 217MPH, but what does MPH stand for? Metres Per Hour ☐ Minutes of Heat ☐ or Miles Per Hour ☐?

7. What is the metal tube or tubes at the back of each vehicle which lets out the fuel burned by the engine? Is it an Exhaust ☐ ☐ a Clutch ☐ or a Spoiler ☐?

8. What is the name of the Hot Wheel ideally designed to compete in drag races?

9. Which is the quickest car to reach 0-60MPH? URBAN AGENT ☐ or TWIN MILL ☐?

10. What colour are the flames that feature over the black paintwork on BONE SHAKER? Yellow ☐ or ☐ red?

11. How many wheels does MED EVIL have?

12. Who has the bigger engine, ULTRA RAGE or SUZUKA?

13. What is the name of the hood which most Hot Wheels engines are underneath? A bonnet ☐ or a boot ☐?

14. A really quick acceleration, similar to the 3.1 SECS it takes RODGER DODGER to go from 0-60MPH, sometimes causes car tyres to squeak and smoke, what's this called... A wheel whizz ☐, a wheel spin ☐ or a wheel heat ☐?

15. BULLY GOAT has a top speed over 250MPH, true ☐ or false ☐?

16. When a driver doesn't need to change through the gears manually, what is the car called, an automatic ☐ and or an easy drive ☐?

17. When a vehicle crosses the finishing line at the end of a race, what's the name of flag that's waved? A patterned flag ☐ zig-zagged flag ☐ or chequered flag ☐?

18. When turning left or right what are the flashing lights called that are used to show other drivers where the car is going? The Indecisions ☐ or the Indicators ☐?

19. Which is the correct spelling of this Hot Wheel... PARRADOCS ☐ or PARADOX ☐?

20. What number appears on the doors of CIRCLE TRACKER? 33 ☐ or 66 ☐?

HAVE YOU EVER DREAMT UP THE PERFECT RACE TRACK FOR YOUR FAVOURITE HOT
WHEELS CARS, WITH TIGHT BENDS, TRICKY CHICANES AND BREATHTAKING STRAIGHTS?
THINK ABOUT WHERE THE TRACK WILL START AND FINISH, CONSIDER WHERE

DRAW YOUR OWN
RACE

PIT LANES AND GARAGES WILL GO, WHILST TRYING TO MAKE IT AS FAST AND EXCITING AS POSSIBLE. REMEMBER, YOU CAN ADD BRIDGES, TUNNELS AND SAND OR GRAVEL BANKS AT THE SIDE OF THE TRACK FOR SAFETY.

TRACK

ROAD SIGNS QUIZ

When drivers are whizzing around the racetrack, there aren't many road signs they need to be aware of. But when you're on the road there are plenty. Some of them are more obvious than others, but how much do you know about driving theory? Work your way through these 10 questions and pick the right option for each.

A) GIVE WAY
B) DEAD END
C) NO ENTRY

A) NO ENTRY
B) NATIONAL SPEED LIMIT APPLIES
C) NO OVERTAKING

A) SCHOOL CROSSING
B) DROP-OFF POINT
C) TAXI-RANK AHEAD

A) UNEVEN ROAD
B) ROAD NARROWS
C) STOP

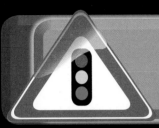

A) SLOW DOWN
B) PEDESTRIAN CROSSING
C) TRAFFIC LIGHTS AHEAD

A) NO SKIDDING
B) SLIPPERY SERVICE
C) DOUBLE CURVE

A) A SPEED LIMIT OF 30 MILES PER HOUR
B) MINIMUM SPEED OF 30 MPH
C) NO MORE THAN 30 CARS ALLOWED ON THIS ROAD AT ONE TIME

A) TURN AROUND
B) ROUNDABOUT
C) CHECK YOUR STEERING WHEEL

A) WATCH OUT FOR OIL LEAKS
B) ICE ON THE ROAD
C) SLIPPERY ROAD

A) INCREASE YOUR SPEED
B) STEEP HILL UPWARDS
C) REVERSE DOWN THE HILL

NAME THE TOOLS

NOW IT'S TIME TO TAKE A LOOK BEHIND THE SCENES AND STEP INTO THE GARAGE. EACH HOT WHEELS CAR IS A HIGHLY TUNED MACHINE AND THE DRIVERS RELY ON THE VERY BEST MECHANICS TO KEEP THE ENGINE PURRING. THESE MECHANICS USE A WHOLE HOST OF DIFFERENT TOOLS. GET YOUR OVERALLS AND LOOK THROUGH THE TEN PICTURES ACROSS THE NEXT PAGE, FILLING IN THE BLANKS TO IDENTIFY WHICH TOOL AND PARTS ARE WHICH...TEN TOOLS AND PARTS...

1.
_ _ _ _ _ _ _

HAMMER SPANNER DRILL
LAMP NUT
JACK SCREWDRIVER
WRENCH
ALLOY WHEEL TYRE

2.
_ _ _ _ _ _

5.
_ _ _ _

8.
_ _ _ _ _ _ _ _

3.
_ _ _ _

6.
_ _ _ _ _

9.
_ _ _

4.
_ _ _ _

7.
_ _ _ _ _
_ _ _ _ _

10.
_ _ _ _ _ _ _ _ _ _ _

MATCH THE CAR
TO ITS CORRECT NAME

Look through the cool pictures of these 10 HOT WHEELS. Check the list of names and match them to the correct car.

RAT BOMB   BONE SHAKER

PROTOTYPE   MERCY BREAKER

FAST FISH ROCKET BOX

NITRO   SPINE BUSTER

CIRCLE TRACKER   BASSLINE

HOT WHEELS
24-hour race

Welcome to the Hot Wheels 24 Hour Race, a marathon driving challenge where the cars drive all through the night and into the day. With hundreds of laps ahead, challenging even the most talented drivers and the most durable cars, there may be a few early exits along the way.

FEATURED CARS

HOT WHEELS
OFFICIAL DRIVER

URBAN AGENT

TOP SPEED: 203 MPH
0-60MPH: 3.8 SECS
ENGINE: V8
POWER: 346 BHP

HOT WHEELS
OFFICIAL DRIVER

SUZUKA

TOP SPEED: 199 MPH
0-60MPH: 3.8 SECS
ENGINE: V12
POWER: 505 BHP

OFFICIAL DRIVER

PARADOX

TOP SPEED: 210 MPH
0-60MPH: 3.2 SECS
ENGINE: V12
POWER: 440 BHP

OFFICIAL DRIVER

ROCKET FIRE

TOP SPEED: 204 MPH
0-60MPH: 3.7 SECS
ENGINE: V8
POWER: 411 BHP

OFFICIAL DRIVER

TWIN MILL

TOP SPEED: 195 MPH
0-60MPH: 3.2 SECS
ENGINE: V8
POWER: 650 BHP

As darkness fell at the Hot Wheels 24 Hour Arena, the fans were crammed into the grandstands and ready to see the cars race through the night, into the morning and into the following evening. The mechanics had worked tirelessly and the drivers had undertaken months of training. The five cars on the grid had different strengths but were all capable of winning. The large engine inside Suzuka's bonnet, and the car's power,

MADE IT AN IDEAL CANDIDATE FOR THE RACE. TWIN MILL AND PARADOX HAD GREAT ACCELERATION. WHILST THE HIGH HORSE POWER OF URBAN AGENT AND ROCKET FIRE MADE THEM IDEAL FOR THE CHALLENGES AHEAD.

IN SUCH A LONG RACE, A QUICK START WOULDN'T BE CRUCIAL, BUT THE DRIVERS WERE READY FOR ACTION. AS THE RED LIGHTS TURNED TO GREEN, THE SMOKE ROSE UP FROM THE TRACK AND ALL FIVE CARS LURCHED FORWARD.

PARADOX TOOK AN EARLY LEAD, FOLLOWED CLOSELY BY TWIN MILL AS THEY REACHED THE FIRST CORNER. BOTH DRIVERS APPEARED HAPPY WITH THEIR START AND WITH SO MANY LAPS LEFT TO GO THEY DIDN'T JOCKEY FOR POSITION TOO MUCH. ROCKET FIRE BROUGHT UP THE REAR AND WAS PROBABLY CARRYING THE MOST FUEL, WHICH MADE IT HEAVIER AND A LOT SLOWER. THE DRIVER STRUGGLED TO TAKE THE TIGHTER BENDS.

TWO HOURS INTO THE RACE AND PARADOX CAME INTO THE PIT LANE FOR SOME LENGTHY MECHANICAL WORK. AS WELL AS A CHANGE OF TYRES AND FUEL TOP UP, SOME SERIOUS WORK WAS NEEDED UNDER THE BONNET.

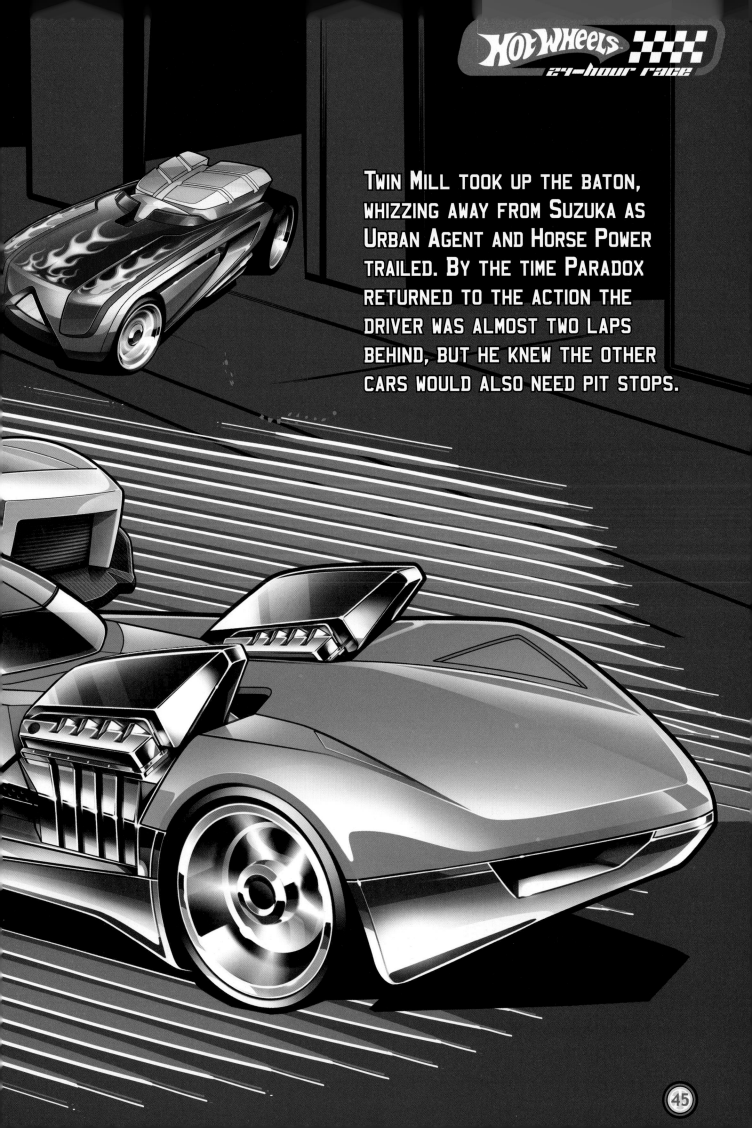

TWIN MILL TOOK UP THE BATON, WHIZZING AWAY FROM SUZUKA AS URBAN AGENT AND HORSE POWER TRAILED. BY THE TIME PARADOX RETURNED TO THE ACTION THE DRIVER WAS ALMOST TWO LAPS BEHIND, BUT HE KNEW THE OTHER CARS WOULD ALSO NEED PIT STOPS.

As they went through the pitch black tunnels the floodlights reflected off each car's paintwork. Rocket Fire overtook Suzuka and Urban Agent. Five hours into the day-long challenge the drivers were settling into a slower rhythm, eager to protect their engines and conserve fuel. Rocket Fire still led but Paradox was second.

SMASH-

As the half-way point approached, disaster struck for Urban Agent and Twin Mill as they clipped wheels on a tight bend. Both vehicles spun violently. Twin Mill crashed into the tyre wall and although the driver was unharmed, the car could not continue.

Urban Agent slid onto the gravel at the side of the track as the driver struggled to keep control. The driver managed to guide his car into the pits but the team decided to retire Urban Agent early.

JUST THREE VEHICLES REMAINED – SUZUKA, ROCKET FIRE AND PARADOX. AS THE SUN ROSE THERE WAS PLENTY OF DISTANCE BETWEEN EACH CAR. ROCKET FIRE LED FROM PARADOX AND THEN SUZUKA.

WITH JUST SIX HOURS REMAINING AND HAVING JUST REFUELLED, THE DRIVER OF PARADOX DECIDED TO MAKE HIS MOVE. HE TOOK MORE RISKS ON BENDS, BRAKED LATER GOING INTO THE TURNS AND TOOK THE RACING LINE WHEN POSSIBLE. ON THE STRAIGHTS HE REALLY BURNED RUBBER AND WITHIN 20 MINUTES HE WAS RIGHT BEHIND ROCKET FIRE'S BUMPER.

THIS SALE
1968

ROCKET FIRE WAS EATING UP THE LAPS WITH ITS POWERFUL V8 ENGINE. PARADOX AND SUZUKA WOULD NEED TO MAKE THEIR MOVE SOON OR RISK LOSING THE RACE.

SEEING PARADOX IN HIS MIRROR, THE DRIVER OF ROCKET FIRE KNEW IT WOULD BE A TIGHT FINISH. AS HE TOOK THE NEXT BEND, SUZUKA WAS RIGHT IN FRONT OF HIM, READY TO BE LAPPED. ALL THREE CARS WERE WITHIN TOUCHING DISTANCE FOR THE FIRST TIME IN HOURS.

THE DRIVER OF SUZUKA HUGGED THE LEFT SIDE OF THE TRACK AND ALLOWED BOTH VEHICLES TO PASS. SUZUKA NEEDED A LENGTHY PIT STOP SO IT NOW LOOKED LIKE A RACE BETWEEN ROCKET FIRE AND PARADOX.

PARADOX'S DRIVER TOOK THE LEAD IN THE PENULTIMATE LAP AFTER A RISKY BUT SUCCESSFUL DRIVING MANOEUVRE LEFT ROCKET FIRE TRAILING IN HIS WAKE.

IT LOOKED LIKE IT WOULD BE HIS RACE FOR THE TAKING. BUT ON THE FINAL BEND STEAM GASSED OUT OF THE ENGINE. THE DRIVER TRIED TO STAY AHEAD OF ROCKET FIRE BUT WAS FIGHTING A LOSING BATTLE.

WINNER!

AS THE FINISHING LINE APPROACHED AND WITH ONE FINAL PIECE OF ACCELERATION ROCKET FIRE LAUNCHED PAST PARADOX AND TOOK THE CHEQUERED FLAG.

RACING
WORLDTOUR
FILL IN YOUR PASSPORT

It's time for the Hot Wheels World Tour! We're about to jet off around the world to show off the finest Hot Wheels machines to motor racing fans in many different countries. Whilst we're there we'll check out the coolest cars and learn a bit about each country.

Before we hit the departure lounge, you'll need to make sure your passport is all filled in and up-to-date...

HOT WHEELS passport

INSERT YOUR PICTURE HERE

SURNAME:
. . . .

FIRST NAME:
. . . .

NATIONALITY:
. . . .

DATE OF BIRTH:
. . . .

SEX (MALE OR FEMALE):
. . . .

PLACE OF BIRTH
. . . .

SIGNATURE:
. . . .

RACING
WORLDTOUR

ENGLAND

FIRST STOP ON THE TOUR IS ENGLAND, A COUNTRY FAMOUS FOR SOME GREAT CLASSIC CARS OVER THE YEARS, INCLUDING JAGUAR, ROLLS ROYCE AND BENTLEY.

PROFILE...

CONTINENT: EUROPE   CAPITAL CITY: LONDON   LANGUAGE: ENGLISH
FAMOUS CARS: JAGUAR, ROLLS ROYCE, BENTLEY, LOTUS
MOST SIMILAR HOT WHEELS: CIRCLE TRACKER

USA

FOR THE FINAL LEG OF OUR WORLD TOUR WE'RE OFF TO THE HOME OF HOT WHEELS, THE UNITED STATES OF AMERICA. THE US IS FAMOUS FOR A NUMBER OF TOP-CLASS CARS, INCLUDING CHEVROLET, FORD AND CHRYSLER.

PROFILE...

CONTINENT: NORTH AMERICA
CAPITAL CITY: WASHINGTON DC
LANGUAGE: ENGLISH
FAMOUS CARS: CHEVROLET, FORD AND CHRYSLER
MOST SIMILAR HOT WHEELS: OVER BOARD 454 AND BULLY GOAT

GERMANY

WE'RE OFF ON OUR TRAVELS AGAIN AND STAYING IN EUROPE FOR A VISIT TO GERMANY, A COUNTRY FAMOUS FOR ITS AUTOBAHN MOTORWAYS AND THE CLASSY MERCEDES BENZ CARS.

PROFILE...

CONTINENT: EUROPE
CAPITAL CITY: BERLIN
LANGUAGE: GERMAN
FAMOUS CARS: MERCEDES BENZ, AUDI, BMW, PORSCHE
MOST SIMILAR HOT WHEELS: NITRO DOORSLAMMER, JACK HAMMER AND SUZUKA

FRANCE

NEXT STOP ON THE TOUR IS FRANCE. FAMOUS FOR THEIR FOOD AND FASHION SENSE, THE FRENCH LIKE STYLISH YET ECONOMIC CARS, LIKE RENAULT, PEUGEOT AND CITROEN.

PROFILE...

CONTINENT: EUROPE
CAPITAL CITY: PARIS
LANGUAGE: FRENCH
FAMOUS CARS: RENAULT, PEUGEOT, CITROEN AND BUGATTI
MOST SIMILAR HOT WHEELS: BASSLINE AND HARD DRIVE

ITALY

THE FIRST DESTINATION OF THE HOT WHEELS WORLD EXHIBITION TOUR IS ITALY. A COUNTRY FAMOUS FOR LUXURIOUS AND POWERFUL SPORTS CARS, THE HOT WHEELS SUPERCARS SHOULD BE RIGHT AT HOME IN ITALY.

PROFILE...

CONTINENT: EUROPE
CAPITAL CITY: ROME
LANGUAGE: ITALIAN
FAMOUS CARS: FERRARI, LAMBORGHINI
MOST SIMILAR HOT WHEELS: SUZUKA

car chase

ANSWER THE QUESTIONS TO GET AROUND THE BOARD

GENTLEMEN START YOUR ENGINES, THE HOT WHEELS LUCKY DICE 5000 RACE IS ABOUT TO START. YOU WILL NEED A DICE AND BETWEEN 2 AND 4 COUNTERS TO PLAY THIS GAME. PLACE YOUR COUNTERS ON THE STARTING GRID AND TAKE TURNS TO ROLL THE DICE. WHOEVER ROLLS THE HIGHEST NUMBER GOES FIRST. IF YOU LAND ON A GREEN LIGHT GO FORWARD ONE SPACE, IF YOU LAND ON A RED LIGHT, GO BACK ONE SPACE AND IF YOU LAND ON AN AMBER LIGHT READ THE INFO ON THAT SPACE AND FOLLOW THE INSTRUCTIONS.

YOU FORGOT TO FILL YOUR CAR WITH PETROL, GO BACK 2 SPACES

Q

Q

RIDE ON!

BRILLIANT EMERGENCY STOP, MOVE FORWARD 2 SPACES

Q

YOU HAVE A FLAT TYRE MISS ONE TURN

Q

KEEP AN EYE OUT FOR ANY QUESTIONS... GET THEM RIGHT AND YOU EARN ANOTHER TURN.
FIRST ONE ACROSS THE CHEQUERED FLAG AT THE FINISH WINS THE RACE!

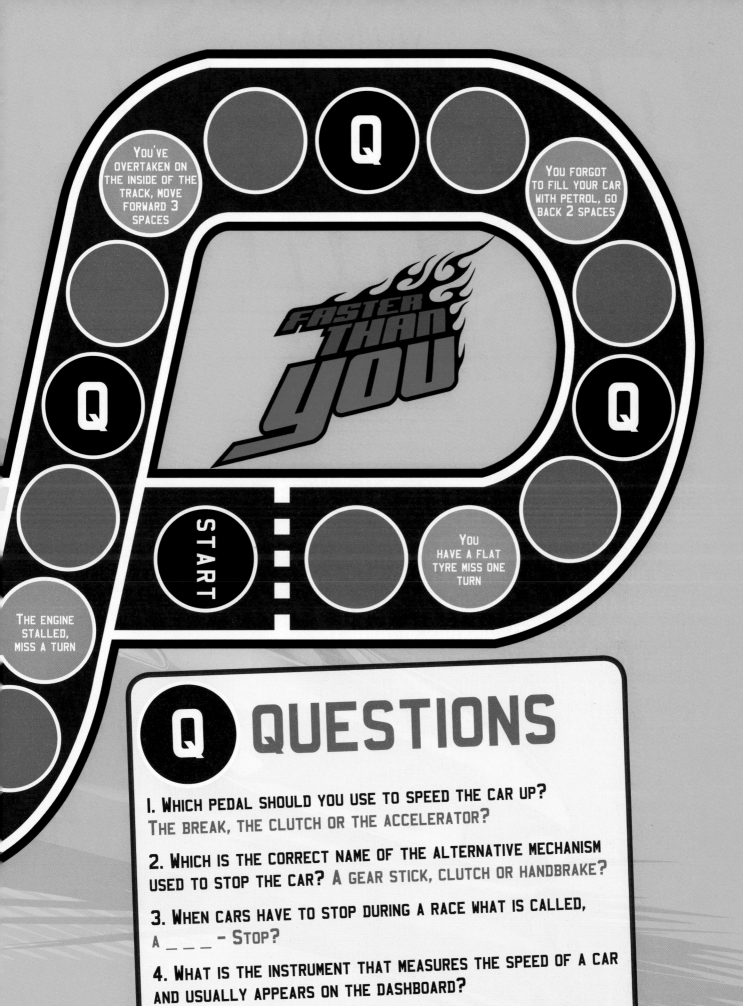

You've overtaken on the inside of the track, move forward 3 spaces

Q

You forgot to fill your car with petrol, go back 2 spaces

Q

Q

START

You have a flat tyre miss one turn

The engine stalled, miss a turn

Q

Q QUESTIONS

1. WHICH PEDAL SHOULD YOU USE TO SPEED THE CAR UP? THE BREAK, THE CLUTCH OR THE ACCELERATOR?

2. WHICH IS THE CORRECT NAME OF THE ALTERNATIVE MECHANISM USED TO STOP THE CAR? A GEAR STICK, CLUTCH OR HANDBRAKE?

3. WHEN CARS HAVE TO STOP DURING A RACE WHAT IS CALLED, A _ _ _ - STOP?

4. WHAT IS THE INSTRUMENT THAT MEASURES THE SPEED OF A CAR AND USUALLY APPEARS ON THE DASHBOARD?

5. WHEN THE TYRES LOCK UP AND THE CAR LOSES GRIP AND SLIDES ACROSS THE TRACK, WHAT IS THIS COMMONLY KNOWN AS?

ANSWERS: 1. ACCELERATOR, 2. HANDBRAKE, 3. A PIT STOP, 4. SPEEDOMETER, 5. A SKID.

OFF-ROAD RALLY

THE FIVE CARS TAKING PART IN THE HOT WHEELS OFF-ROAD RALLY WOULD HAVE TO BE ABLE TO DRIVE OVER ROUGH TERRAIN, THROUGH GRAVEL, THICK MUD AND SOMETIMES WATER, ENSURING AN EXCITING AND UNPREDICTABLE RACE. THE FANS GATHERED IN THEIR THOUSANDS AROUND THE FOREST COURSE TO WATCH THESE FIVE DREAM MACHINES ACCELERATE THROUGH THE GEARS IN A RACE AGAINST THE CLOCK AND EACH OTHER.

END OF THE ROAD

THE CARS...

ROCKET BOX

Top Speed:	160 MPH
0-60:	3.4 SECS
Engine:	V6
Power:	650 BHP

CIRCLE TRACKER

Top Speed:	175 MPH
0-60:	4.6 SECS
Engine:	V6
Power:	356 BHP

FAT FISH

Top Speed:	180 MPH
0-60:	4.5 SECS
Engine:	V8
Power:	360 BHP

COOL ONE

Top Speed:	206 MPH
0-60:	4.3 SECS
Engine:	V12
Power:	445 BHP

BULLY GOAT

Top Speed:	203 MPH
0-60:	4.5 SECS
Engine:	V6
Power:	510 BHP

THE HOT WHEELS OFF ROAD RALLY WOULD PROVIDE AN EXTREMELY DIFFERENT CHALLENGE TO THE CARS. THIS WAS NOT JUST ABOUT SPEED AND PERFORMANCE, THE ABILITY OF THE CARS TO DRIVE ON HARDER AND SOFTER TERRAIN WOULD ALSO PROVE CRUCIAL.

THE RALLY WAS HELD AT A THICK EVERGREEN FOREST IN THE HEART OF SCANDINAVIA. A DELUGE OF RAIN HAD FOLLOWED A FRESH FROST ON THE MORNING OF

THE RACE BUT A LARGE CROWD HAD GATHERED IN EAGER ANTICIPATION OF THE DAY'S RACING.

THE FIVE VEHICLES TAKING PART WERE ROCKET BOX, CIRCLE TRACKER, FAT FISH, COOL ONE AND BULLY GOAT. ALL OF THE CARS HAD DIFFERENT STRENGTHS AND THE DRIVERS WOULD HAVE TO BE AT THEIR BEST TO GUIDE THEM AROUND THE TWISTS AND TURNS OF A MUDDY AND WET TRACK.

SOME OF THE CORNERS WERE EXTREMELY TIGHT AND AT CERTAIN POINTS THE CARS WOULD FLY THROUGH THE AIR AFTER HITTING HILLS AND SLOPES AT HIGH SPEEDS.
THE RACE WOULD WORK ON A TIME TRIAL BASIS WITH EACH CAR TAKING TURNS TO COMPLETE A LAP OF THE RALLY CIRCUIT.
THE QUICKEST VEHICLE WOULD BE THE WINNER.

FIRST UP WAS THE POWERFUL BULLY GOAT WHO SKIDDED AWAY DOWN THE TRACK AS THE GRAVEL AND MUD SPAN UP INTO THE AIR. THE DRIVER, WHO WAS JOINED BY A NAVIGATOR, GUIDED THE VEHICLE THROUGH PUDDLES AND PATCHES OF MUD AS THEY ENTERED THE FOREST. SPECTATORS SOUNDED HORNS AND APPLAUDED AS BULLY GOAT TORE AROUND THE COURSE IN AN IMPRESSIVE 2 MINUTES AND 37 SECONDS.

NEXT TO TAKE THE TRACK WAS CIRCLE TRACKER. WITH LESS POWER AND A LOWER TOP SPEED THAN BULLY GOAT, CIRCLE TRACKER'S DRIVER STRUGGLED TO MAKE A QUICK START. AS THE RAIN CAME DOWN, THE CAR'S WINDSCREEN WIPERS BATTLED AT FULL FORCE AS THE DRIVER BATTLED TO SEE WHERE HE WAS GOING.

CIRCLE TRACKER REVVED PAST THE FIRST CHECKPOINT IN 44 SECONDS. THROUGH THE WOODED AREA OF THE COURSE, CIRCLE TRACKER WAS EVEN SLOWER AND THE DRIVER ALMOST SKIDDED OFF THE MUDDY TRACK ON SEVERAL OCCASIONS. EVENTUALLY THE MUD-COVERED MACHINE CROSSED THE FINISHING LINE IN 3 MINUTES AND 3 SECONDS.

THE DRIVER OF FAT FISH REVVED THE POWERFUL V8 ENGINE AS THE RACE OFFICIAL WAVED THE STARTING FLAG THEN HIS CAR SHOT THROUGH WATER PUDDLES AND MUD TRAPS WITH EASE. THE CAR CROSSED THE FIRST CHECKPOINT IN RECORD TIME, WITH HIS 37 SECONDS THE QUICKEST FIRST LEG SO FAR. THE TIGHT GRAVEL BENDS WEREN'T PROVING TOO MUCH OF A PROBLEM, NEITHER WERE THE LARGE BRANCHES WHICH HAD FALLEN ONTO THE TRACK.

AFTER GETTING PLENTY OF AIR FROM THE FINAL HILL AND LANDING WITH A SPLASH INTO A LARGE MUD PUDDLE, FAT FISH WAS LOOKING A FEW SECONDS QUICKER THAN LEADER BULLY GOAT AND EVENTUALLY PASSED THE CHEQUERED FLAG IN 2 MINUTES AND 34 SECONDS TO TAKE THE LEAD.

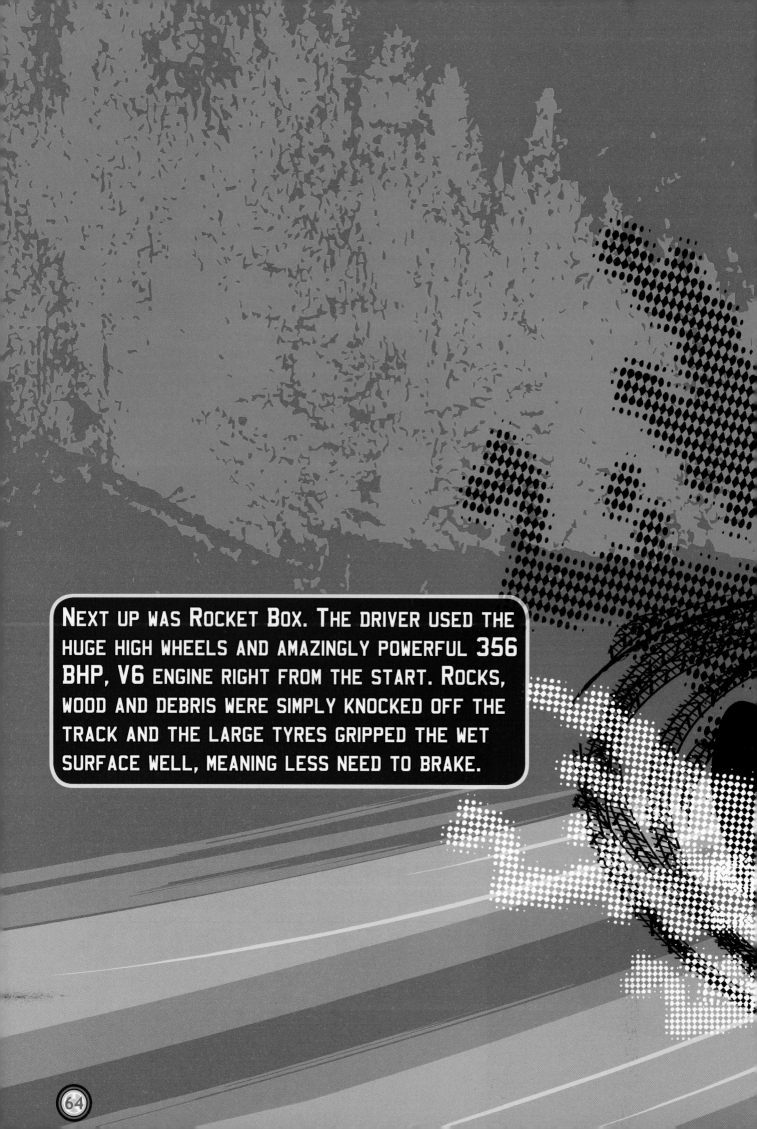

NEXT UP WAS ROCKET BOX. THE DRIVER USED THE HUGE HIGH WHEELS AND AMAZINGLY POWERFUL 356 BHP, V6 ENGINE RIGHT FROM THE START. ROCKS, WOOD AND DEBRIS WERE SIMPLY KNOCKED OFF THE TRACK AND THE LARGE TYRES GRIPPED THE WET SURFACE WELL, MEANING LESS NEED TO BRAKE.

At the end of the first leg, Rocket Box matched Fat Fish's time of 37 seconds but at the second checkpoint he was ahead, clocking 1 minute and 7 seconds. Everything was looking good, until the driver slightly misjudged a turn and skidded up an embankment and into a ditch. Rocket Box's large, powerful wheels helped the driver back on course but crucial seconds were lost and the finish time was 2 minutes and 35 seconds, one second off top spot!

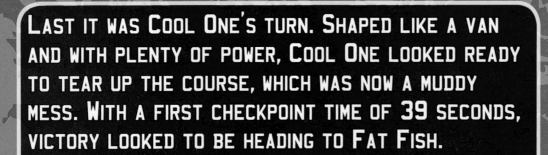

LAST IT WAS COOL ONE'S TURN. SHAPED LIKE A VAN
AND WITH PLENTY OF POWER, COOL ONE LOOKED READY
TO TEAR UP THE COURSE, WHICH WAS NOW A MUDDY
MESS. WITH A FIRST CHECKPOINT TIME OF 39 SECONDS,
VICTORY LOOKED TO BE HEADING TO FAT FISH.

THE DRIVER OF COOL ONE PUT HIS PEDAL TO THE METAL
THROUGH THE TOUGH WOODLAND SECTION AND PASSED
THROUGH THE SECOND LEG IN 1 MINUTE AND 5 SECONDS.

IF THE DRIVER COULD KEEP THAT SPEED UP HE'D FINISH FIRST BUT THE TIGHT GRAVEL BENDS WERE STILL AHEAD. HOWEVER, HE DROVE THROUGH THE TWISTS AND TURNS PERFECTLY. AS THE CAR CRASHED BACK DOWN ON THE TRACK AFTER THE BIGGEST HILL, THE ENGINE ROARED INTO ACTION FOR THE FINAL STRAIGHT AS COOL ONE CROSSED THE LINE IN 2 MINUTES AND 25 SECONDS, CLAIMING FIRST AND THE HOT WHEELS OFF ROAD RALLY TROPHY.

ANSWERS

P13. LABEL THE CAR PARTS
1. TYRE, 2. ENGINE, 3. WINDSCREEN,
4. DRIVER-SIDE DOOR, 5. BONNET,
6. WHEEL, 7. SPOILER

P15. HOT WHEELS NAME MIX UP
1. SURF CRATE, 2. ULTRA RAGE,
3. RAT BOMB, 4. ZOTIC, 5. COOL ONE,
6. SUZUKA, 7. URBAN AGENT, 8. SPINE
BUSTER, 9. TWIN MILL, 10. 24 SEVEN

P16. SPOT THE DIFFERENCE

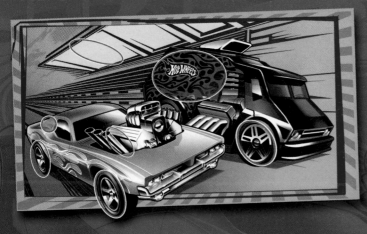

P17. BUMPER WORDSEARCH

S	F	H	V	N	E	N	I	G	N	E	P	I
C	L	J	S	F	D	L	T	X	S	T	E	L
B	L	E	D	W	O	Z	A	E	S	T	E	B
I	I	B	E	R	L	B	S	R	W	U	Q	A
C	O	P	T	H	E	L	E	Y	F	D	S	X
Q	Y	E	O	V	W	P	W	U	S	T	S	W
C	P	K	L	P	I	Y	T	T	E	D	S	T
H	Y	M	D	W	U	J	E	P	T	Z	Y	E
U	O	V	B	N	M	J	D	T	S	R	N	L
Y	R	C	V	I	S	D	F	G	E	J	K	S
P	T	E	N	P	I	Y	T	R	F	V	M	T
E	P	B	V	S	D	L	L	E	M	O	I	H
X	R	A	D	I	A	T	O	R	C	J	R	G
H	B	N	M	H	G	V	F	T	Y	U	R	I
A	D	L	C	S	K	A	E	R	B	D	O	L
U	T	I	N	K	L	P	O	P	S	X	R	F
S	G	N	K	K	L	O	D	W	U	E	F	X
T	G	H	J	S	Y	V	B	N	S	T	I	P
L	E	E	H	W	G	N	I	R	E	E	T	S
S	J	F	N	E	E	R	C	S	D	N	I	W
S	P	G	E	A	R	S	V	B	N	K	L	L

P32. HOT WHEELS CAR QUIZ
1. ZOTIC, 2. V12, 3. COOL ONE,
4. PURPLE PASSION, 5. BRAKE HORSE
POWER, 6. MILES PER HOUR,
7. EXHAUST, 8. DRAGSTER, 9. TWIN
MILL, 10. RED, 11. FOUR, 12. SUZUKA – V12
ENGINE, 13. BONNET, 14. WHEEL SPIN,
15. FALSE, 16. AUTOMATIC,
17. CHEQUERED FLAG, 18. INDICATORS,
19. PARADOX, 20. 33

P36. ROAD SIGNS QUIZ
1. NO ENTRY, 2. NATIONAL SPEED LIMIT
APPLIES, 3. SCHOOL CROSSING,
4. ROAD NARROWS, 5. TRAFFIC LIGHTS
AHEAD, 6. DOUBLE CURVE,
7. A SPEED LIMIT OF 30 MILES PER HOUR,
8. ROUNDABOUT, 9. SLIPPERY ROAD,
10. STEEP HILL UPWARDS

P38. NAME THE TOOLS
1. SPANNER, 2. HAMMER, 3. JACK,
4. TYRE, 5. LAMP, 6. DRILL,
7. ALLOY WHEEL, 8. SPANNER, 9. NUT,
10. SCREWDRIVER

P39. MATCH THE CAR TO ITS CORRECT NAME

PROTOTYPE   RAT BOMB
MERCY BREAKER   BONE SHAKER
FAST FISH   SPINE BUSTER
NITRO   BASSLINE
CIRCLE TRACKER   ROCKET BOX